It is kite day at Pine Lake.
Can you fly a kite?

Jeff's kite is wide.
It is a big size.
Jeff's kite is fun to fly.

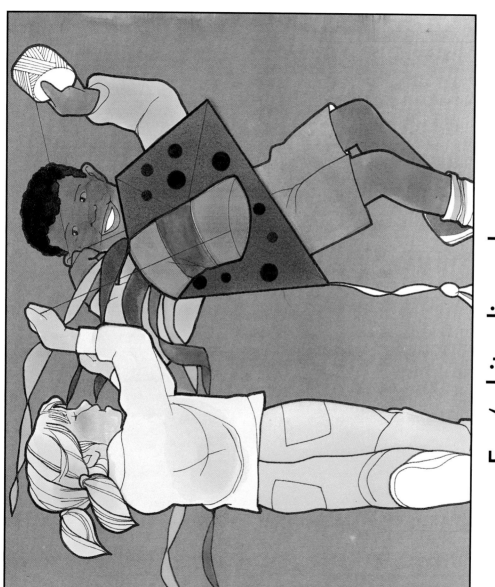

Fay's kite dives down.
It dives by Ike's kite.
Ike's kite is red with dots.

Jan's kite is fine.
It has five sides.
It is a nice kite.

Bob sees the kites.
He is sad.
Bob has no kite to fly.

The kids make a kite for Bob.
Jan cuts out the kite.

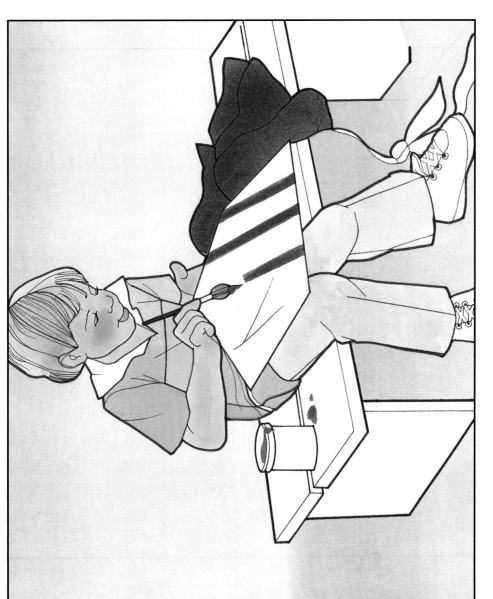

Jeff makes lines on Bob's kite.
It is white with lines.

Nine kites fly at Pine Lake.
The kites dip and rise.
Nine kids smile.